Contents

Adjectives

(Tune: *I Saw Three Ships* Track 1)

Adjectives are rather clever
Add a noun, they work together
What you get is quite exciting
It's descriptive writing

Let me show you how to do it
Really there is nothing to it
Adjectives make nouns exciting
It's descriptive writing

Take a path and make it *rough*
Try a quiz and find it *tough*
Take a house and make it *creepy*
Look the baby is *sleepy!*

Take a car and make it *blue*
Try a dress and make it *new*
Take a cat and make it *lazy*
Look your brother is *crazy!*

Take a ring and make it *old*
Try a river and make it *cold*
Take a dog and make it *spotty*
Look your nose is *snotty!*

Adjectives are rather clever
Add a noun, they work together
What you get is quite exciting
It's descriptive writing

Adverbs

(**Tune:** *Horsey Horsey* Track 2)

If you're walking down the street
How are you moving your two feet?
Describe the verbs it's such great fun
Adverbs interest everyone

You're walking *quickly*, you're feeling *sickly*
What a useful little word!
You're laughing *madly*, you're limping *badly*
There are so many adverbs to be heard

If you're studying in your class
How are you making sure you pass?
Describe the verbs it's such great fun
Adverbs interest everyone

You're reading *nicely*, you're writing *precisely*
What a useful little word!
You're working *neatly*, you're talking *sweetly*
There are so many adverbs to be heard

Adverbs, adverbs always fun
So many ways to get things done
Calmly, clearly, fairly, soon
Join in with this adverb tune!

Capital Letters

(**Tune:** *Wee Willie Winkie* Track 3)

Capital letters
Where should they be?
Listen very carefully
When you start a sentence
Use one, nice and tall
Capitals are letters that are tallest of them all

Capital letters
Where should they be?
Listen very carefully
When you start a name
Use one, it is best
Capitals are letters that are taller than the rest

Capital letters
Where should they be?
Listen very carefully
When you write a title
One should start each word
Using only lower case is really quite absurd!

Comparatives and Superlatives

(**Tune:** *Sing a Song of Sixpence* Track 4)

Comparatives are useful, they help you to compare
Two objects or items, you need to be aware
If they both are strong but one of them is more
That one is the *stronger*, of that we can be sure

So if you want to say that anything is more
Add the letters *e-r*, that is what they're for
Taller or *softer*, *bigger* you can see
Putting *e-r* on the end is certainly the key

Superlatives are useful, they help you to compare
Two or more items, you need to be aware
If they all are heavy but one of them the most
Then it is the *heaviest* but there's no need to boast

So if you want to say that the most is what you've got
Add the letters *e-s-t*, just give it a shot
Tallest or *softest*, *biggest* you can see
Add *e-s-t* on the end, I think that you'll agree

Compound Words

(Tune: *I Am the Music Man* Track 5)

I am a compound word
I'm clever as can be
There are two words
And they make me
They're joined together

Join *light* and *house* to make *lighthouse*
Make *lighthouse*, make *lighthouse*
Join *light* and *house* to make *lighthouse*
Light and *house* - *lighthouse!*

I am a compound word
I'm clever as can be
There are two words
And they make me
They're joined together

Join *foot* and *ball* to make *football*
Make *football*, make *football*
Join *foot* and *ball* to make *football*
Foot and *ball* - *football!*

Join *light* and *house* to make *lighthouse*
Make *lighthouse*, make *lighthouse*
Join *light* and *house* to make *lighthouse*
Light and *house* - *lighthouse!*

I am a compound word
I'm clever as can be
There are two words
And they make me
They're joined together

Join *sun* and *flower* to make *sunflower*
Make *sunflower*, make *sunflower*
Join *sun* and *flower* to make *sunflower*
Sun and *flower* - *sunflower!*

Join *foot* and *ball* to make *football*
Make *football*, make *football*
Join *foot* and *ball* to make *football*
Foot and *ball* - *football!*

Join *light* and *house* to make *lighthouse*
Make *lighthouse*, make *lighthouse*
Join *light* and *house* to make *lighthouse*
Light and *house* - *lighthouse!*

I am a compound word
I'm clever as can be
There are two words
And they make me
They're joined together

Join *skate* and *board* to make *skateboard*
Make *skateboard*, make *skateboard*
Join *skate* and *board* to make *skateboard*
Skate and *board* - *skateboard!*

Join *sun* and *flower* to make *sunflower*
Make *sunflower*, make *sunflower*
Join *sun* and *flower* to make *sunflower*
Sun and *flower* - *sunflower!*

Join *foot* and *ball* to make *football*
Make *football*, make *football*
Join *foot* and *ball* to make *football*
Foot and *ball* - *football!*

Join *light* and *house* to make *lighthouse*
Make *lighthouse*, make *lighthouse*
Join *light* and *house* to make *lighthouse*
Light and *house* - *lighthouse!*

Conjunctions

(Tune: *The Grand Old Duke of York* Track 6)

Oh, my sentence has two parts
That I don't want to split
I need to join them up somehow
So let's get on with it

Conjunction time again
Conjunction time again
It's time to use a joining word
Conjunction time again

I use 'and' all the time
More than I think I should
Time to use another word
To make my writing good

Conjunction time again
Conjunction time again
It's time to use a joining word
Conjunction time again

Why not try 'because'
Or maybe try 'although'
'Whether' is another one
Or 'for' or 'but' or 'so'

Conjunction time again
Conjunction time again
It's time to use a joining word
Conjunction time again
Conjunction time again!

Contractions

(Tune: *The Bear Went Over the Mountain* Track 7)

Contractions are so clever
They join words together
Replacing missing letters
With an apostrophe

You need not say 'do not'
Look at what you've got
You can take out a letter
'Don't' sounds much better
Replace the missing letter
With an apostrophe

Contractions are so clever
They join words together
Replacing missing letters
With an apostrophe

You needn't say 'let us'
Why have all that fuss?
You can take out a letter
'Let's' sounds much better
Replace the missing letter
With an apostrophe

Dictionary

(Tune: *Dance to Your Daddy* Track 8)

Dictionary
It's necessary
Helps with your writing
When you can't spell words

If you cannot spell it
Look it up and tell it
Words are all in order
Of the alphabet

Dictionary
It's necessary
Gives definitions
Of an unknown word

If you do not know it
Look it up and show it
Words are all in order
Of the alphabet

Dictionary
It's necessary
Keep one beside you
When you read and write

All the words are listed
They are never twisted
A to Z you'll find them
Alphabetical

Dictionary
It's necessary
Don't be without one
Learning words is fun

Dictionary
It's necessary
Don't be without one
Learning words is fun

Homophones

(Tune: *Oh Dear, What Can the Matter Be?* Track 9)

Oh dear, what can the matter be?
Homophones are always confusing me
Sounding alike, but it is quite clear to see
They are such different words

I *read* a whole book with a cover so *red*
I *ate* up *eight* burgers I was over-fed
The wind *blew* the *blue* scarf right over my head
These are such different words!

Oh dear, what can the matter be?
Homophones, they are spelled differently
Meanings aren't the same, it is clear to see
They are such different words

I spotted a *bear* that had fur that was *bare*
I tried not to *stare* when I tripped up the *stair*
The *hare* ran so fast that it whipped up my *hair*
These are such different words!

Oh dear, what can the matter be?
Homophones are always confusing me
Sounding alike, but it is quite clear to see
They are such different words

Magic e

(Tune: *Miss Polly Had a Dolly* Track 10)

Have you heard of a magic e
It changes sounds so easily
It sits on the end of a word like 'cop'
And sends its magic over with a hop

The magic makes the vowel say its name
So the word will never ever be the same
With a spark of magic *hop* turns into *hope*
Pip turns to *pipe* and *cop* to *cope*

Hop-over e works on short vowel sounds
And changes them to long ones with some leaps and bounds
Turn *cub* to *cube* and *hat* to *hate*
The magic e will help you and you'll think it's great!

Nouns

(Tune: *Baa Baa Black Sheep* Track 11)

In your sentence, can you use a noun?
Yes, and I can write it down
One for an object and one for a name
One for a place or date, now you do the same

Common nouns are everywhere you look
Objects like a chair or book
If it's one to touch or see
A common noun it will certainly be

Proper nouns are something with a name
A person, place, or date or game
Choose a name that you like better
And start it with a capital letter

In your sentence, can you use a noun?
Yes, and I can write it down
One for an object and one for a name
One for a place or date, now you do the same

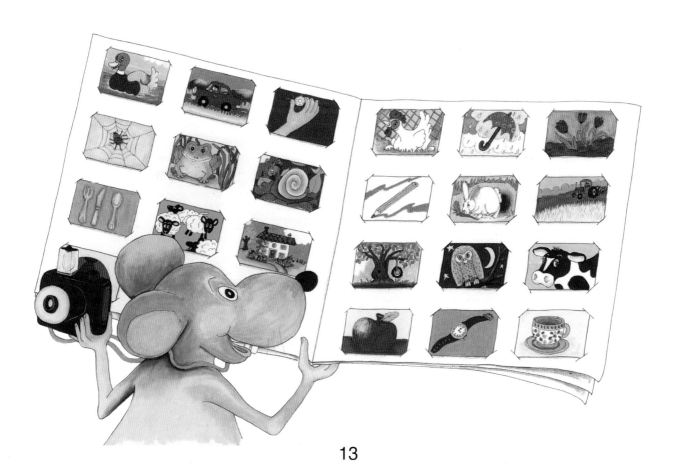

Past, Present and Future Tense

(**Tune:** *The Hokey Cokey* Track 12)

Think about last year
About last week
Yesterday
Let me hear you shout
It's already happened
So it's in the past
That's what its all about

Oh, the past tense
Oh, it makes sense
Oh, the past tense
It's already happened
Ra! Ra! Ra!

Think about today
About just now
Right this moment
Let me hear you shout
It's happening this minute
So it's in the present
That's what it's all about

Oh, the present tense
Oh, it makes sense
Oh, the present tense
It's happening this minute
Ra! Ra! Ra!

Think about next year
About next week
Some time later
Let me hear you shout
It's happening tomorrow
So it's in the future
That's what it's all about

Oh, the future tense
Oh, it makes sense
Oh, the future tense
It's going to happen
Ra! Ra! Ra!

Time is split
In different ways
Past, present, future
Let me hear you shout
When is something happening?
You must decide
That's what it's all about

Past, present and future
Past, present and future
Past, present and future
When's it happening?
Ra! Ra! Ra!

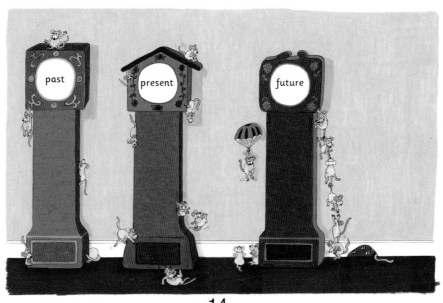

Plurals

(**Tune:** *My Bonnie Lies Over the Ocean* Track 13)

Let's talk about making things plural
It means having more than one thing
If there's thirteen or twenty or fifty
It's time that we all start to sing

Add 's'
Add 's'
It turns one thing into much more
For sure
Add 's'
Add 's'
It turns one thing into much more

Let's talk about making things plural
There's one more thing before you go
If the word ends with *sh* or *ch*
Or an *s* or an *x* then you know

Add 'es'
Add 'es'
It turns one thing into much more
For sure
Add 'es'
Add 'es'
It turns one thing into much more

So now practise making things plural
Turn one hat into many hats
Turn one box into lots of boxes
And one rat into several rats

Add 's'
Add 's'
It turns one thing into much more
For sure
Add 'es'
Add 'es'
It turns one thing into much more

15

Prefixes and Suffixes

(**Tune:** *Do Your Ears Hang Low?* Track 14)

It's a prefix song
Why don't you sing along
Put one at the front
Of a word where it belongs
So the word will change
You don't need to find it strange
It's a prefix song

Take a word like *kind*
Add a prefix and you'll find
That the word can change
To something like *unkind*
It's the meaning that has changed
As the word is rearranged
But we never mind!

It's a prefix song
Why don't you sing along
Put one at the front
Of a word where it belongs
So the word will change
You don't need to find it strange
It's a prefix song

Take a word like *take*
Add a prefix and you'll make
The entire word change
To something like *mistake*
It's the meaning that has changed
As the word is rearranged
Well for goodness sake!

It's a suffix song
Why don't you sing along
Put one at the end
Of a word where it belongs
So the word will change
You don't need to find it strange
It's a suffix song

Take a word like *do*
Add a suffix, why don't you
And the word can change
To *doing* it is true
It's the meaning that has changed
As the word is rearranged
You should try one too!

It's a suffix song
Why don't you sing along
Put one at the end
Of a word where it belongs
So the word will change
You don't need to find it strange
It's a suffix song

Take a word like *ill*
Add a suffix, yes you will
And the word can change
To *illness* what a thrill
It's the meaning that has changed
As the word is rearranged
It's a clever skill!

Prepositions

(**Tune:** *Michael Finnegan* Track 15)

I want to use a preposition
It will tell me the position
Over, under, inside, outside
Mission preposition

It is certainly worth knowing
Where exactly something's going
Is it *through, along* or *nearby?*
Mission preposition

It is only right and fitting
That I know where someone's sitting
Underneath or right *behind* me
Mission preposition

I have noted down and jotted
Where the object can be spotted
Up or *down* or right *beside* you
Mission preposition

Prepositions always know
Whereabouts a noun will show
Or where it is going to go
Mission preposition

I want to use a preposition
It will tell me the position
Over, under, inside, outside
Mission preposition

Pronouns

(**Tune:** *Aiken Drum* Track 16)

There are a group of words that are
Quite personal, quite personal
Don't go searching very far
Just look at *you* and *me*

Introducing pronouns, pronouns, pronouns
Personal pronouns
Including *you* and *me*

Repeating names is such a fuss
Is such a fuss, is such a fuss
Use a pronoun - *them* or *us*
Or *I* or *he* or *she*

Introducing pronouns, pronouns, pronouns
Personal pronouns
Including *you* and *me*

Pronouns take the place of nouns
The place of nouns, the place of nouns
Never any ups or downs
With *it* or *they* or *we*

Introducing pronouns, pronouns, pronouns
Personal pronouns
Including *you* and *me*

There are a group of words that are
Quite personal, quite personal
Don't go searching very far
Just look at *you* and *me*

Introducing pronouns, pronouns, pronouns
Personal pronouns
Including *you* and *me*

Introducing pronouns, pronouns, pronouns
Personal pronouns
Including *you* and *me*

Punctuation

(**Tune:** *Happy and you Know It* Track 17)

Use a comma between items in a list
Use a comma between items in a list
Then you'll see what you have got
Plus the things that you have not
Use a comma between items in a list

Use a full stop and the reader knows to stop
Use a full stop and the reader knows to stop
Your sentence is done
So why not have some fun
Use a full stop and the reader knows to stop

When you're asking something, use a question mark
When you're asking something, use a question mark
It's good to know the answer
So don't be a chancer
When you're asking something, use a question mark

Use an exclamation mark to show surprise
Use an exclamation mark to show surprise
Or you may want to shout
So just let it out
Use an exclamation mark to show surprise

You can make your writing great - punctuate!
You can make your writing great - punctuate!
You can cause a sensation
If you use punctuation
So make your writing great and punctuate!

You can make your writing great - punctuate!
You can make your writing great - punctuate!
You can cause a sensation
If you use punctuation
So make your writing great and punctuate!

Speech Marks

(Tune: *Pop Goes the Weasel* Track 18)

Speech marks make it loud and clear
The words that will be spoken
Opening and closing marks
The rules can't be broken

Place them at the front of speech
And also at the end
Sit them high above the line
It's what I recommend

Opening speech marks they come first
Then a capital letter
Closing speech marks round it off
Make them neat, it's better

If you can remember this
You are clever sparks
Punctuation must be placed
Before the closing speech marks

Use an exclamation mark
If you want to yell
Question marks are also good
Commas work as well

Speech marks make it loud and clear
The words that will be spoken
Opening and closing marks
The rules can't be broken

Thesaurus
(Synonyms and Antonyms)

(Tune: *She'll Be Coming Round the Mountain* Track 19)

I would like to tell you of a special book
And then you can all go and take a look
It's a book that just can't bore us
It's called a thesaurus
It's full of words, one glance and you'll be hooked!

Oh yes, thesaurus is its name
And to reassure us is its game
It will help you find new words
That is what I've heard
So now it's time for you to do the same

It is very good if you would like to find
Words with meanings of a similar kind
Like 'sparkle', 'shine' and 'glow'
Or 'leave', 'depart' and 'go'
The list of choices gives you peace of mind

How about another little game
Can you find some words that aren't the same?
Like matching 'hot' with 'cold'
Or matching 'new' with 'old'
Finding opposites can be your aim

Oh yes, thesaurus is its name
And to reassure us is its game
It will help you find new words
That is what I've heard
So now it's time for you to do the same

21

Verbs

(Tune: *Girls and Boys Come Out to Play* Track 20)

Have you heard of 'doing' words?
They are also known as verbs
Verbs are active, verbs are fun
See if you can look out for one

Girls and boys they like to *play*
Dancers like to *swish* and *sway*
Horses like to *jump* and *trot*
Lions like to *roar* a lot

Teachers like to *help* and *care*
Friends they like to *give* and *share*
Spiders like to *crawl* and *creep*
Babies like to go to *sleep*

Cleaners like to *scrub* and *wash*
Swimmers like to *splash* and *splosh*
Workmen like to *dig* and *drill*
Chefs they like to *bake* and *grill*

Anything that you can do
To *laugh*, to *walk*, to *work*, to *chew*
All of these are doing words
Now you know a lot of verbs

Games and Activities

Musical Parts of Speech

1 Allocate each corner of the room (or garden) to a particular part of speech: noun, verb, adjective, adverb etc, any combination is fine. Play some music and the players dance in the middle of the room. When the music stops, the adult calls out a word and the players must race to the corner they think correctly relates to the word. For example, if the adult calls 'green' the players should rush to the 'adjective' corner. The last player to reach the corner is out of the game, as is anyone who runs to the wrong corner. The winner is the last remaining player.

Dreamy Definitions

2 Player one looks through the dictionary for a word that they think player two (or more players) won't know the meaning of. Player one writes the real definition of the word on one piece of paper and, on a separate piece of paper, writes down a definition that they have made up. They can make it as funny as they like! Player two should try and guess which definition is the real one and if they guess correctly, they earn a point. If they don't manage it, player one earns the point for their great made-up definition. Then it is player two's turn to choose a word. See which player can score the most points.

Time Travel Designer

3 Take a piece of paper and fold it into three sections. Label each section 'Past', 'Present' and 'Future'. Now choose something to design, such as a car. In the 'Past' section, draw an old car from a time in history, perhaps even the first car that was invented! In the 'Present' section, draw a car that we use nowadays, perhaps your own family car. In the 'Future' section, have fun designing what you think cars will look like in the future. Perhaps they will hover above the road and no longer need wheels! You can really use your imagination.

Games and Activities

Homophone Memory Matching

4 Think of as many pairs of homophones as you can and draw pictures of them on separate pieces of paper. When you have finished, mix them up and place them all face down on the table or on the floor. With a friend, take it in turns to turn two pictures over at a time and see if you have a homophone match. If you do, you can keep that pair. If you don't then you must turn both pictures over again and try to remember where they were for next time. When all the pairs have been found, the winner is the player who has the most pairs of homophones.

Compound Collection

5 Think of a compound word and write the first part of it on one piece of card and the second part on another. For example, write 'sun' on one piece and 'flower' on another. Do this for as many compound words as you can think of. Shuffle the cards and deal out five cards to both players. The remaining pile of cards should be placed face down between the players. Each player should look at their cards and see if they can make a compound word using two of them. If they can, they should lay the word down in front of them. After this, players take turns in picking the top card off the pile and seeing if they can use it with one of their existing cards to make a compound word. If they can use it they may keep the card and place a card they don't want on the bottom of the pile. If they can't use it, they place it straight on the bottom of the pile. The winner is the first player to make four compound words.

Adverb Antics

6 Cut up some strips of paper and write a different adverb on each one. On separate strips of paper, write some verbs. Place the verbs and adverbs in separate containers. The players take it in turns to pick one verb and one adverb, put them together, and act out the result. For example, if 'walk' and 'quickly' were picked out, the player should demonstrate walking quickly around the room. Lots of fun can be had with the various combinations that can be picked out.